My Last Writes

The Ultimate End of Life Planning Workbook for Your Family

This Book Belongs to: ______________________________

Dated: ________________

Revised Date: ____________

Revised Date: ____________

Revised Date: ____________

Revised Date: ____________

My Last Writes -The Ultimate End of Life Planning Workbook for Your Family

ISBN: 978-0-578-76079-7

Table of Contents

Introduction

It's an uncomfortable subject and one most prefer to avoid discussing, but death is inevitable and like most things in life one must prepare for that as well. Finally, *My Last Writes* is now available to assist you in defining your last wishes in a comprehensive fill-in workbook that covers everything from how you want your service performed to information regarding your financial matters to pet care after you're gone. Unfortunately, many families are unprepared without the slightest notion of what to do, how to do it, and who to contact to assist them in getting the answers they will desperately need.

While your funeral may be decades away, planning now relieves your family of making quick and uninformed decisions. *My Last Writes* will prompt many thoughts and details you might have overlooked in your own advanced planning without the assistance of these guided pages. This workbook is comprehensive and you are likely to encounter some questions that may not relate to your circumstances or you may simply choose to skip over some questions, if so, just move on to the next.

My Last Writes also includes a section offering an opportunity to complete personal statements along with a section to write love letters that you can share with your loved ones. Imagine everything your family will need to know in just one book written in your hand. What could be a better legacy! *My Last Writes* will undoubtedly offer peace of mind to you knowing your loved ones will know exactly what to do to avoid family conflict and guesswork by writing down everything they'll need to know including your final wishes, what needs to be done, where to find everything, and direction from you for your family so they can manage their affairs seamlessly after you're gone.

• • •

* Complete your workbook in pencil and update regularly.

* This book is not meant to replace your Will; however, it will include everything else your family will need to know.

* It's important to leave your *My Last Writes* workbook with a trusted loved one, your Executor or your Will attorney because much of the information will need to be known **immediately**. You may wish to place the sensitive information such as passwords or account numbers in a separate safe place and note who will have access when needed.

Personal Information

Full Legal Name: ____________________

Maiden Name: ____________________

Phone: __________ Cell: __________ Email: __________

Home Address: ____________________

Mailing Address: ____________________

Date of Birth:__________ Place of Birth: __________

Social Security Number: __________

Driver's License Number: __________ State: _____ Expiration: _____

Organ Donor: Yes: _____ No: _____

Passport Number: __________ Country: _____ Expiration: _____

Nationality: __________ US Citizen: Yes: _____ No: _____

Green Card: Yes: _____ No: _____ Naturalization Number: __________

Marital Status: Single: ____ Married: ____ Divorced: _____ Widowed: _____

Name of Spouse: __________ Address: __________

Phone: __________ Cell: __________ Email: __________

Person(s) With a Copy of This Book:

Name: __________ Relationship: __________

Phone: __________ Cell: __________ Email: __________

Contact Person if I Become Incapacitated:

Primary: __________ Relationship: __________

Phone: __________ Cell: __________ Email: __________

Secondary: __________ Relationship: __________

Phone: __________ Cell: __________ Email: __________

Employment

Current Employer: ____
Address: ____
Job Title: _______________ Department: __________ Start Date: _________

Benefits:
Life Insurance Yes: _____ No: _____
Profit Sharing Yes: _____ No: _____
Pension Fund Yes: _____ No: _____
Union Plan Yes: _____ No: _____
Shareholder Yes: _____ No: _____

Previous Employment

Previous Employer: ____
Address: ____
Job Title: _______________ Department: ______________
Start Date: __________ Ended: _________ Retirement: _____________

Benefits:
Life Insurance Yes: _____ No: _____
Profit Sharing Yes: _____ No: _____
Pension Fund Yes: _____ No: _____
Union Plan Yes: _____ No: _____
Shareholder Yes: _____ No: _____

NOTES ____

Family Information

Father Living: Yes No

Name:______________________ Email: ______________________

Ph/Cell: ______________________ Address: ______________________

Mother Living: Yes No

Name:______________________ Email: ______________________

Ph/Cell: ______________________ Address: ______________________

Children

Name: ______________________ Email: ______________________

Ph/Cell: ______________________ Address: ______________________

Name: ______________________ Email: ______________________

Ph/Cell: ______________________ Address: ______________________

Name: ______________________ Email: ______________________

Ph/Cell: ______________________ Address: ______________________

Name: ______________________ Email: ______________________

Ph/Cell: ______________________ Address: ______________________

Name: ______________________ Email: ______________________

Ph/Cell: ______________________ Address: ______________________

Name: ______________________ Email: ______________________

Ph/Cell: ______________________ Address: ______________________

Name: ______________________ Email: ______________________

Ph/Cell: ______________________ Address: ______________________

Name: ______________________ Email: ______________________

Ph/Cell: ______________________ Address: ______________________

Name: ______________________ Email: ______________________

Ph/Cell: ______________________ Address: ______________________

Family Information

Grandchildren

Name: ____________________ Name:____________________ Name: ____________________
Name: ____________________ Name:____________________ Name: ____________________
Name: ____________________ Name:____________________ Name: ____________________
Name: ____________________ Name:____________________ Name: ____________________
Name: ____________________ Name:____________________ Name: ____________________

Step-Family

Name: ____________________________ Email: ______________________________
Ph/Cell: ___________________________ Relationship: _______________________

Name: ____________________________ Email: ______________________________
Ph/Cell: ___________________________ Relationship: _______________________

Name: ____________________________ Email: ______________________________
Ph/Cell: ___________________________ Relationship: _______________________

Name: ____________________________ Email: ______________________________
Ph/Cell: ___________________________ Relationship: _______________________

Name: ____________________________ Email: ______________________________
Ph/Cell: ___________________________ Relationship: _______________________

NOTES ____

People Dependent Upon Me

Dependent: ______________ Contact Person: ________________
Relationship: ______________ Ph: ___________ Email: _______________________

Dependent: ______________ Contact Person: ________________
Relationship: ______________ Ph: ___________ Email: _______________________

Dependent: ______________ Contact Person: ________________
Relationship: ______________ Ph: ___________ Email: _______________________

Dependent: ______________ Contact Person: ________________
Relationship: ______________ Ph: ___________ Email: _______________________

Dependent: ______________ Contact Person: ________________
Relationship: ______________ Ph: ___________ Email: _______________________

Dependent: ______________ Contact Person: ________________
Relationship: ______________ Ph: ___________ Email: _______________________

Dependent: ______________ Contact Person: ________________
Relationship: ______________ Ph: ___________ Email: _______________________

Dependent: ______________ Contact Person: ________________
Relationship: ______________ Ph: ___________ Email: _______________________

NOTES ____

Emergency Contact Numbers

Accountant
Firm: ____________________ Accountant: ______________________________
Ph: ______________________ Email: __________________________________

Attorney
Firm: ____________________ Attorney: _______________________________
Ph: ______________________ Email: __________________________________

Executor
Name: ___________________ Relationship: ____________________________
Ph: ______________________ Email: __________________________________

Financial Planner
Firm: ____________________ Planner: ________________________________
Ph: ______________________ Email: __________________________________

Funeral Home
Name: ___________________ Director: ________________________________
Ph: ______________________ Email: __________________________________

Life Insurance Agent
Agency: _________________ Agent: __________________________________
Ph: ______________________ Email: __________________________________

Clergy
Religious Affiliation: _______ Clergyperson: ___________________________
Ph: ______________________ Email: __________________________________

Primary Physician
Name: ___________________ Ph: _________________

Other
Name: ___________________ Relationship: ____________________________
Ph: ______________________ Email: __________________________________

Will and Designated Powers

Will: Yes: ___ No: ___ Dated: _________ Location: _________________

Will/Trust Attorney: ___________ Ph: _________ Email: _________________

Person with a Copy: _________________ Relationship: ____________________
Ph: ________________________________ Email: ____________________________

Living Will: Yes: _____ No: ______ Location: ____________________________

Durable Power of Attorney Regarding Health Care Matters
Health Care Surrogate: _____________________ Ph: ____________________
Location of Document: _____________________ Relationship: ______________

Organ Donation
Organ Donor Yes: _____ No: _____ Location of Documentation: ____________

Donate Body for Medical Education: Yes: _____ No: _____
Name of Medical School/Research Institution: _________________________________
Location of Documentation: ____

****Typically, research institutions will cremate the remains for the family once the research is complete.***

DNR Order: Yes: _____No: _____ Designee: ________________ Ph: ____________
****The DNR order is a separate form not included in your Living Will or Advanced Directive.***

Palliative Care: Yes: _____ No: ______ Location of Documentation:_____________

Durable Power of Attorney Regarding Financial Matters
Designee: _____________________ Relationship: _________________________
Ph: ___________________________ Email: ______________________________

Advanced Directive: Yes: _____ No: ______ Location: _______________________

****In order to create an Advanced Directive, you will need to use your state's particular forms:***
http://everplans.com/node/666 ***Additional Information:*** www.aarp.org

NOTES

Final Arrangements

The Person in Charge of Making Funeral Arrangements
Name: ____________________ Ph: ____________ Email: __________________________

Prearrangements: Yes: ____ No: ____ Prepaid: Yes: _____ No: _____
Location of Contract: __________________ Website: _______________________

Funeral Home: ___________ Address: ____
Director: __________________ Ph: ____________ Email: __________________________

Life Insurance Agency: _____________________ Website:_______________________
Agent: ____________________ Ph: ____________ Email: __________________________
Policy Number: ____________________________ Value: __________________________
Beneficiary: _______________ Ph: ____________ Email: __________________________

Life Insurance Agency: _____________________ Website:_______________________
Agent: ____________________ Ph: ____________ Email: __________________________
Policy Number: ____________________________ Value: __________________________
Beneficiary: _______________ Ph: ____________ Email: __________________________

Life Insurance Agency: _____________________ Website:_______________________
Agent: ____________________ Ph: ____________ Email: __________________________
Policy Number: ____________________________ Value: __________________________
Beneficiary: _______________ Ph: ____________ Email: __________________________

Types of Services

1. Traditional Funeral
2. Memorial Services
3. Graveside Service

Types of Funerals

1. Traditional Religious
2. Non-Religious Humanist
3. Direct Cremation
4. Green Natural Burial (No Casket)
5. Military Service
6. Burial at Sea

Final Arrangements

Person to Conduct Ceremony

Name: ______________________________ Title: ______________________________

Ph: ______________________ Email: ____

Person to Deliver the Eulogy

Name: ______________________________ Relationship: ________________________

Ph: ______________________ Email: ____

Other Speakers

Speaker: ___________________________ Relationship: ________________________

Ph: ______________________ Email: ____

Speaker: ___________________________ Relationship: ________________________

Ph: ______________________ Email: ____

Songs/Hymns

1. __________________________________ 4. __________________________________
2. __________________________________ 5. __________________________________
3: __________________________________ 6. __________________________________

Scriptures or Readings

1. __________________________________ 4. __________________________________
2. __________________________________ 5. __________________________________
3. __________________________________ 6. __________________________________

Flowers Arranged by Funeral Home: Yes:____ No:____

Type: ____________________________________ Prepaid: Yes: _____ No: _____

Disposition of Flowers after the Service: ____________________________________

____

____

NOTES ____

____

____

Final Arrangements

Donations Requested in Lieu of Flowers
List Agency(s)
1. ______________________________ Ph: ________________
2. ______________________________ Ph: ________________
3. ______________________________ Ph: ________________
4. ______________________________ Ph: ________________

Memorial Service Yes: _____ No: _____ Rosary Yes: ____ No: _____
Reception Yes: _____ No: _____ Meal Yes: ____ No: _____
Wake Yes: _____ No: _____ Potluck Yes: ____ No: _____
Shiva Yes: _____ No: _____ Refreshments Yes: ____ No: _____

Reception Location: ________________ Address: ____________________

Casket Model Number: ________________ Open: _____ Closed: _____

Cremation: Yes: _____ No: _____ Prepaid: Yes: _____ No: _____

Crematory: ________________ Address: ____________________

Ph: ________________ Location of Contract: ____________

Urn Selection: ________________ Prepaid: Yes: _____ No: _____

Ashes Present at Service: Yes: ____ No: _____

Scatter Garden: Yes: ____ No: _____ Location: ____________________

Cemetery: ________________ Address: ____________________

Plot Location Number: ______________ Prepaid: Yes: ____ No: ____

Type of Grave Marker: ______________ Prepaid: Yes: ____ No: ____

Mausoleum Entombment: Yes: ____No: ____ Prepaid: Yes: ____ No: ____

Inscription: ____
____
____

Final Arrangements

Clothing to Be Worn : ____

____

Jewelry to Be Worn: Yes: _____ No: _____
If yes, Details: ____

____

Traditional Religious Service
Place of Worship: ____________________ Address: ____________________

Non-Religious/Humanist Service
Location: ____________________ Address: ____________________

Gravesite Service Location: ____

Military Service: Yes: _____ No: _____ Branch: ____________________

Military Affiliations to Attend the Service (Ex: U.S. Army, VFW, Veteran Assn., etc.)

Name: ______________ Contact Person: ______________ Ph: ______________

Name: ______________ Contact Person: ______________ Ph: ______________

Name: ______________ Contact Person: ______________ Ph: ______________

NOTES ____

____

____

____

____

____

____

____

____

____

____

*** *When family members make your final arrangements at the time of death, expenses tend to be more costly.***

Final Arrangements

Alternate Burial Options

Green Natural Burial: Yes: ____ No: ____ Pre-Paid: Yes: ___ No: ___
Company to Perform Service: __________________ Ph: __________________________
Location of Pre-Paid Contract: _________________ Website: ___________________

Burial at Sea: Yes: ____ No: ____ Pre-Paid: Yes: ___ No: ___
Company to Perform Service: __________________ Ph: __________________________
Location of Pre-Paid Contract: _________________ Website: ___________________

NOTES ____

** By arranging and pre-paying your funeral services, you'll have a contract with fixed fees that will not increase at the time of your death.*

Final Arrangements

Pallbearers

Name: ____________________ Ph: ____________ Email: __________________________

Name: ____________________ Ph: ____________ Email: __________________________

Name: ____________________ Ph: ____________ Email: __________________________

Name: ____________________ Ph: ____________ Email: __________________________

Name: ____________________ Ph: ____________ Email: __________________________

Name: ____________________ Ph: ____________ Email: __________________________

Name: ____________________ Ph: ____________ Email: __________________________

Name: ____________________ Ph: ____________ Email: __________________________

NOTES ____

Obituary Guidelines

Suggested details to include in an obituary

Photograph
Name: Include Nicknames, Sr., Jr., Dr., Etc.
Age
Address: Include City and State
Cause of Death
Place of Death: Home, Hospital, Nursing Home, Etc.
Date of Birth
Date of Death
Parents: Father-Mother, Include Maiden Name
Education
Occupation
Offices Held: Boards Served on, Etc.
Military Service: Rank Held
Clubs, Organizations, Hobbies, Etc.
Personal Attributes
Predeceased by: Include Immediate Family
Survivors: Include City and State
Visitation: Include Date, Time and Place
Shiva: Include Date, Time and Place
Wake: Include Date, Time and Place
Service: Include Date, Time, Place
Reception: Include Information: Location, Lunch, Buffet, Potluck, etc.
List Pall Bearers
Memorial Suggestions: List Preferred Organizations
Indicate Newspaper(s) You Want Your Obituary Published
List Organizations to Donate to In Lieu of Sending Flowers
Include Additional Information Deemed Important by The Family

The Person I Want to Write My Obituary:

Name: ______________________ Relationship: ________________________
Ph: ________________________ Email: ____________________________

Obituary

Self-Written

Memorialized Facebook Page

Legacy Contact: ________________ Relationship: ____________________________

Ph: ____________ Cell: ________________ Email: _______________________________

Delete Account: Yes: ___ No: ___

Memorialize Account: Yes: ___ No: ___ Duration: ___________________

Requested Cover Photo: (Describe Photo to insert) ____

Message to Display: ____

____

A Few Ideas to Honor Your Loved Ones:

1. Give to the loved one's favorite charity
2. Plant a tree in their honor
3. Plan a celebration of their life
4. Purchase a memorial bench or marker in their name
5. Get a tattoo--a permanent reminder of your loved one

NOTES ____

____

____

____

____

____

____

____

____

____

____

____

____

____

____

People to Notify

Name: ____________________ Ph: ___________ Email: ________________________
Name: ____________________ Ph: ___________ Email: ________________________
Name: ____________________ Ph: ___________ Email: ________________________
Name: ____________________ Ph: ___________ Email: ________________________

Name: ____________________ Ph: ___________ Email: ________________________
Name: ____________________ Ph: ___________ Email: ________________________
Name: ____________________ Ph: ___________ Email: ________________________
Name: ____________________ Ph: ___________ Email: ________________________

Name: ____________________ Ph: ___________ Email: ________________________
Name: ____________________ Ph: ___________ Email: ________________________
Name: ____________________ Ph: ___________ Email: ________________________
Name: ____________________ Ph: ___________ Email: ________________________

Name: ____________________ Ph: ___________ Email: ________________________
Name: ____________________ Ph: ___________ Email: ________________________
Name: ____________________ Ph: ___________ Email: ________________________
Name: ____________________ Ph: ___________ Email: ________________________

Name: ____________________ Ph: ___________ Email: ________________________
Name: ____________________ Ph: ___________ Email: ________________________
Name: ____________________ Ph: ___________ Email: ________________________
Name: ____________________ Ph: ___________ Email: ________________________

Name: ____________________ Ph: ___________ Email: ________________________
Name: ____________________ Ph: ___________ Email: ________________________
Name: ____________________ Ph: ___________ Email: ________________________
Name: ____________________ Ph: ___________ Email: ________________________

Small Gifts

(Mementos not included in my Will I want my loved ones to have.)

Name: ______________________ Relationship: ______________________
Ph: ______________________ Email: ______________________
Items: ____
____

Name: ______________________ Relationship: ______________________
Ph: ______________________ Email: ______________________
Items: ____
____

Name: ______________________ Relationship: ______________________
Ph: ______________________ Email: ______________________
Items: ____
____

Name: ______________________ Relationship: ______________________
Ph: ______________________ Email: ______________________
Items: ____
____

Name: ______________________ Relationship: ______________________
Ph: ______________________ Email: ______________________
Items: ____
____

Name: ______________________ Relationship: ______________________
Ph: ______________________ Email: ______________________
Items: ____
____

Name: ______________________ Relationship: ______________________
Ph: ______________________ Email: ______________________
Items: ____
____

Name: ______________________ Relationship: ______________________
Ph: ______________________ Email: ______________________
Items: ____
____

Small Gifts

(Mementos not included in my Will I want my loved ones to have.)

Name: ______________________ Relationship: ______________________
Ph: ______________________ Email: ______________________
Items: ____

Name: ______________________ Relationship: ______________________
Ph: ______________________ Email: ______________________
Items: ____

Name: ______________________ Relationship: ______________________
Ph: ______________________ Email: ______________________
Items: ____

Name: ______________________ Relationship: ______________________
Ph: ______________________ Email: ______________________
Items: ____

Name: ______________________ Relationship: ______________________
Ph: ______________________ Email: ______________________
Items: ____

Name: ______________________ Relationship: ______________________
Ph: ______________________ Email: ______________________
Items: ____

Name: ______________________ Relationship: ______________________
Ph: ______________________ Email: ______________________
Items: ____

Name: ______________________ Relationship: ______________________
Ph: ______________________ Email: ______________________
Items: ____

Disposition of My Remaining Belongings

Person to Dispose of Household Items and Clothing Not Included in My Will:

Name: ______________________ Relationship: ______________________

Ph: __________ Cell: __________ Email: ____________________________

Name: ______________________ Relationship: ______________________

Ph: __________ Cell: __________ Email: ____________________________

Donate Remainder of Items to the Following Agencies:(Ex: Salvation Army, Komen Fdn.)

1. ____________________________ Ph: ____________________
2. ____________________________ Ph: ____________________
3. ____________________________ Ph: ____________________
4. ____________________________ Ph: ____________________

NOTES ____

Location of Important Documents

Will: ________________________________

Power of Attorney: ________________________________

Living Will/Health Care Directives: ________________________________

Funeral Planning Documents: ________________________________

Birth Certificate: ________________________________

Marriage Certificate: ________________________________

Divorce Agreement: ________________________________

Income Tax Records: ________________________________

Driver's License: ________________________________

Organ/Body Donor Card: ________________________________

Passport: ________________________________

Immigration Documents: ________________________________

Citizenship Documents: ________________________________

Life Insurance Policies: ________________________________

Real Estate Deeds: ________________________________

Vehicle Titles: ________________________________

Partnership Contract: ________________________________

Business Contracts: ________________________________

Articles of Incorporation: ________________________________

Loan Contracts: ________________________________

Loans Due Me Contracts: ________________________________

Other Monies Owed Me: ________________________________

Other: ________________________________

Other: ________________________________

Other: ________________________________

Location of Valuable Property

Jewelry: ______________________________

Cash: ______________________________

Gold and Silver: ______________________________

Firearms: ______________________________

Personal Effects: ______________________________

Hidden Valuables: ______________________________

Heirlooms: ______________________________

Other: ______________________________

Other: ______________________________

Other: ______________________________

A Few Collection Examples

Stamp	Toy	Fossil	Video Game
Coin	Doll	Painting	Baseball Card
Gun	Wine	Watch	Comic Book
Car	Fine Art	Element	Sports Memorabilia
Book	Antique	Vinyl Record	Commemorative
Dish			

Contents in My Safe Deposit Box

Bank: ______________________________

Address: ______________________________

1. ______________________________
2. ______________________________
3. ______________________________
4. ______________________________
5. ______________________________
6. ______________________________
7. ______________________________
8. ______________________________
9. ______________________________
10. ______________________________

It's amazing how often people hide cash and valuables in their homes and in the most inconspicuous places. It's best to share your location with someone you trust.

Additional Professional Contacts

Attorney/Estate Planner
Firm: ______________________ Attorney: ______________________
Email: ______________________ Ph/Cell: ______________________

Private Banker
Firm: ______________________ Banker: ______________________
Email: ______________________ Ph/Cell: ______________________

Financial Planner
Firm: ______________________ Planner: ______________________
Email: ______________________ Ph/Cell: ______________________

Stock Broker
Firm: ______________________ Broker: ______________________
Email: ______________________ Ph/Cell: ______________________

Insurance Agent
Firm: ______________________ Agent: ______________________
Email: ______________________ Ph/Cell: ______________________

Insurance Agent
Firm: ______________________ Agent: ______________________
Email: ______________________ Ph/Cell: ______________________

Business Partner
Firm: ______________________ Partner: ______________________
Email: ______________________ Ph/Cell: ______________________

Other
Firm: ______________________ Agent: ______________________
Email: ______________________ Ph/Cell: ______________________

Other
Firm: ______________________ Agent: ______________________
Email: ______________________ Ph/Cell: ______________________

Other
Firm: ______________________ Agent: ______________________
Email: ______________________ Ph/Cell: ______________________

NOTES

Real Estate

Primary Mortgage
Mortgage: Yes: ____ No: ____ Paid Off: Yes: ___ No: ___
Lender: __________________ Jointly Owned: Yes: ___ No: ___
Co-Owner: _______________ Ph: ___________ Location of Policy: _______________

Second Mortgage
Mortgage: Yes: ____ No: ____ Paid Off: Yes: ___ No: ___
Lender: __________________ Jointly Owned: Yes: ___ No: ___
Co-Owner: _______________ Ph: ___________ Location of Policy: _______________

Vacation Home
Mortgage: Yes: ____ No: ____ Paid Off: Yes: ___ No: ___
Lender: __________________ Jointly Owned: Yes: ___ No: ___
Co-Owner: _______________ Ph: ___________ Location of Policy: _______________

Condo
Mortgage: Yes: ____ No: ____ Paid Off: Yes: ___ No: ___
Lender: __________________ Jointly Owned: Yes: ___ No: ___
Co-Owner: _______________ Ph: ___________ Location of Policy: _______________

Time Share
Mortgage: Yes: ____ No: ____ Paid Off: Yes: ___ No: ___
Lender: __________________ Jointly Owned: Yes: ___ No: ___
Co-Owner: _______________ Ph: ___________ Location of Policy: _______________

Commercial Property
Mortgage: Yes: ____ No: ____ Paid Off: Yes: ___ No: ___
Lender: __________________ Jointly Owned: Yes: ___ No: ___
Co-Owner: _______________ Ph: ___________ Location of Policy: _______________

Commercial Property
Mortgage: Yes: ____ No: ____ Paid Off: Yes: ___ No: ___
Lender: __________________ Jointly Owned: Yes: ___ No: ___
Co-Owner: _______________ Ph: ___________ Location of Policy: _______________

Real Estate

Rental Property

Mortgage: Yes: ___ No: ____ Paid Off: Yes: ____ No:____

Lender: _________________ Ph: ____________ Email:_______________

Co-Owner: ______________ Ph:_____________ Email:_______________

Tenant: _________________ Ph: ____________ Email:_______________

Manager: ________________ Ph: ____________ Email:_______________

Rental Property

Mortgage: Yes: ___ No: ____ Paid Off: Yes: ____ No:____

Lender: ________________ Ph: ____________ Email:_______________

Co-Owner: _____________ Ph: ____________ Email:_______________

Tenant: ________________ Ph: ____________ Email:_______________

Manager: _______________ Ph: ____________ Email:_______________

Other Property

Mortgage: Yes: ____ No: ____ Paid Off: Yes: ___ No: ___

Lender: __________________ Jointly Owned: Yes: ___ No: ___

Co-Owner: _____________________ Ph: _____ Location of Policy: _________

NOTES ____

____

____

____

____

____

____

____

____

____

____

____

____

____

____

Vehicles

Car
Make: _________ Model: ______________ Year: ____ VIN: _____________________
Loan: Yes: _____ Paid off: Yes: ___ No: ___ Loan Number: ________________
Lender: ___________________ Ph: ____________ Lease: Yes: _____ No: ____

Car
Make: _________ Model: ______________ Year: _____ VIN: _____________________
Loan: Yes: _____ Paid off: Yes: ___ No: ___ Loan Number: ________________
Lender: ___________________ Ph: ____________ Lease: Yes: _____ No: ____

Truck
Make: _________ Model: ______________ Year: _____ VIN: _____________________
Loan: Yes: _____ Paid off: Yes: ___ No: ___ Loan Number: ________________
Lender: ___________________ Ph: ____________ Lease: Yes: _____ No: ____

Motorcycle
Make: _________ Model: ______________ Year: _____ VIN: _____________________
Loan: Yes: _____ Paid off: Yes: ___ No: ___ Loan Number: ________________
Lender: ___________________ Ph: ____________ Lease: Yes: _____ No: ____

RV
Make: _________ Model: ______________ Year: ____ VIN: _____________________
Loan: Yes: _____ Paid off: Yes: ___ No: ___ Loan Number: ________________
Lender: ___________________ Ph: ____________ Lease: Yes: _____ No: ____

Off Road Vehicle
Make: _________ Model: ______________ Year: ____ VIN: _____________________
Loan: Yes: _____ Paid off: Yes: ___ No: ___ Loan Number: ________________
Lender: ___________________ Ph: ____________ Lease: Yes: _____ No: ____

Boat
Make: _________ Model: ______________ Year: ____ HIN: _____________________
Loan: Yes: _____ Paid off: Yes: ___ No: ___ Loan Number: ________________
Lender: ___________________ Ph: ____________ Lease: Yes: _____ No: ____

Liens and Loans

Mechanic Lien Against Me

Lienholder: ____________________ Ph: _______________ Loan Number: _______

Reason for Lien: ________________ Pay off Date: ______ Amount: ___________

Property on Which Lien is Held: ____

Lien Against Me

Lienholder: ____________________ Ph: _______________ Loan Number: _______

Reason for Lien: ________________ Pay off Date: ______ Amount: ___________

Property on Which Lien is Held: ____

Lienholder: ____________________ Ph: _______________ Loan Number: _______

Reason for Lien: ________________ Pay off Date: ______ Amount: ___________

Property on Which Lien is Held: ____

Outstanding Loans I Have

Lender: _______________________ Ph: _______________ Loan Number: _______

Reason for Loan: ________________ Pay off Date: ______ Amount: ___________

Outstanding Loans I Have

Lender: _______________________ Ph: _______________ Loan Number: _______

Reason for Loan: ________________ Pay off Date: ______ Amount: ___________

Judgments Against Me

Name: ________________________ Ph: __________________________

Reason: _______________________ Amount: ______________________

NOTES ____

____

____

____

____

____

** WWW.Annualcreditreport.com is a free comprehensive reporting service that identifies ALL outstanding loans and debts including credit card debt.*

Loans Due Me

Name of Debtor: ________________ Email: ________________________________
Ph: __________________ Address: ________________________________
Loan Amount: ________ Balance: ___________ Interest Rate: ____
Reason for Loan: _________________ Current on Payment: Yes: ____ No: _____
Date of Loan: ____________________ Pay off Date: _________________________
Contract Location: ____
Forgive Loan: Yes: _____ No: _____ Gift Loan to: ___________________________

Name of Debtor: ________________ Email:_________________________________
Ph: __________________ Address: ________________________________
Loan Amount: ________ Balance: ___________ Interest Rate: ____
Reason for Loan: _________________ Current on Payment: Yes: ____ No: _____
Date of Loan: ____________________ Pay off Date: _________________________
Contract Location: ____
Forgive Loan: Yes: _____ No: _____ Gift Loan to: ___________________________

Name of Debtor: ________________ Email:_________________________________
Ph: __________________ Address: ________________________________
Loan Amount: ________ Balance: ___________ Interest Rate: ____
Reason for Loan: _________________ Current on Payment: Yes: ____ No: _____
Date of Loan: ____________________ Pay off Date: _________________________
Contract Location: ____
Forgive Loan: Yes: _____ No: _____ Gift Loan to: ___________________________

NOTES ____

NOTES

Bank Accounts

Checking Account

Name of Bank: ____________________ Location: ________________________________

Name on Account: ________________ Account Number: ________________________

User Name: _______________________ Password/Pin: ____________________________

Savings Account

Name of Bank: ____________________ Location: _______________________________

Name on Account: ________________ Account Number: _______________________

Savings Account

Name of Bank: ____________________ Location: _______________________________

Name on Account: ________________ Account Number: _______________________

ATM Card

Name of Bank: ____________________ Location: ________________________________

Name on Account: ________________ Account Number: ________________________

User Name: _______________________ Password/Pin: ____________________________

Credit Union

Name of Bank: ____________________ Location: ________________________________

Name on Account: ________________ Account Number: ________________________

User Name: _______________________ Password/Pin: ____________________________

Brokerage Account

Name of Bank: ____________________ Location: ________________________________

Name on Account: ________________ Account Number: ________________________

User Name: _______________________ Password/Pin: ____________________________

NOTES ____

____

____

____

____

____

Credit Cards

Name on Card: ______________________
Expiration Date: ______ Security Code: ___
User Name: ___________________________
Card Number: ___________________
Auto Bill Pay: Yes: _____ No: _____
Password: _______________________

Name on Card: ______________________
Expiration Date: ______ Security Code: ___
User Name: ___________________________
Card Number: ___________________
Auto Bill Pay: Yes: _____ No: _____
Password: _______________________

Name on Card: ______________________
Expiration Date: ______ Security Code: ___
User Name: ___________________________
Card Number: ___________________
Auto Bill Pay: Yes: _____ No: _____
Password: _______________________

Name on Card: ______________________
Expiration Date: ______ Security Code: ___
User Name: ___________________________
Card Number: ___________________
Auto Bill Pay: Yes: _____ No: _____
Password: _______________________

Name on Card: ______________________
Expiration Date: ______ Security Code: ___
User Name: ___________________________
Card Number: ___________________
Auto Bill Pay: Yes: _____ No: _____
Password: _______________________

Name on Card: ______________________
Expiration Date: ______ Security Code: ___
User Name: ___________________________
Card Number: ___________________
Auto Bill Pay: Yes: _____ No: _____
Password: _______________________

Name on Card: ______________________
Expiration Date: ______ Security Code: ___
User Name: ___________________________
Card Number: ___________________
Auto Bill Pay: Yes: _____ No: _____
Password: _______________________

Name on Card: ______________________
Expiration Date: ______ Security Code: ___
User Name: ___________________________
Card Number: ___________________
Auto Bill Pay: Yes: _____ No: _____
Password: _______________________

Name on Card: ______________________
Expiration Date: _____ Security Code: ___
User Name: __________________________
Card Number: ___________________
Auto Bill Pay: Yes: _____ No: _____
Password: _______________________

Retirement Accounts

IRA

Name of Institution: ______________ Name on Account: ______________________
Account Number: ________________ Contact: ______________________________
Beneficiary: ____________________ Ph: _____________ Email: ______________

Roth IRA

Name of Institution: ______________ Name on Account: ______________________
Account Number: ________________ Contact: ______________________________
Beneficiary: ____________________ Ph: _____________ Email: ______________

Mutual Funds

Name of Institution: ______________ Name on Account: ______________________
Account Number: ________________ Contact: ______________________________
Beneficiary: ____________________ Ph: _____________ Email: ______________

Mutual Funds

Name of Institution: ______________ Name on Account: ______________________
Account Number: ________________ Contact: ______________________________
Beneficiary: ____________________ Ph: _____________ Email: ______________

Annuity

Name of Institution: ______________ Name on Account: ______________________
Account Number: ________________ Location: _____________________________
Beneficiary: ____________________ Ph: _____________ Email: ______________

Money Market

Name of Bank: __________________ Name on Account: ______________________
Account Number: ________________ Location: _____________________________
Beneficiary: ____________________ Ph: _____________ Email: ______________

Certificate of Deposit

Bank: _________________________ Maturity Date: ____________ Value: _________
Beneficiary:____________________ Ph: _____________ Email: _________________

Retirement Accounts

US Savings Bonds

Name on Account: _______________ Serial Number:_____________ Value: __________

Beneficiary: _____________________ Ph: ___________ Email: ___________________

US Savings Bonds

Name on Account: _______________ Serial Number:_____________ Value: __________

Beneficiary: _____________________ Ph: ___________ Email: ___________________

Employment Pension

Company: ____________________________ Retirement Date: ____________

Monthly Income: ___________________________ Location: ___________________

Transferable Benefits: Yes: _____ No: ____ Beneficiary: _________________

Ph: _______________________ Email: ______________________

Union Pension

Company: ____________________________ Retirement Date: _____________

Monthly Income: ___________________________ Location: ___________________

Transferable Benefits: Yes: _____ No: _____ Beneficiary: __________________

Ph: _______________________ Email: _______________________

Social Security

Name on Account:_____________________ SSN: _______________________

Retirement Date: ______________________ Monthly Income: ____________

Beneficiary: ___________________________ Ph: __________________________

NOTES ____

Veteran's Benefits

Name on Account: ____________________ Account Number: ______________

Monthly Income: ______________________ Serial Number: __________________

Continuing Educational Benefits for Children: Yes: _____ No: ______

Beneficiary: ____________________ Ph: ___________ Email: ____________________

Beneficiary: ____________________ Ph: ___________ Email: ____________________

Beneficiary: ____________________ Ph: ___________ Email: ____________________

Beneficiary: ____________________ Ph: ___________ Email: ____________________

List Additional VA Benefits that Continue after Death for Your Dependents:

1. ____
2. ____
3. ____
4. ____

NOTES ____

Trusts

Trust in Which I Am the Beneficiary

Name of Trust: ________________ Trust Bank: ________________________

Date of Trust: ________________ Location of Document: ________________

Trust Manager: ________________ Ph: __________ Email: ________________

Beneficiary: __________________ Ph: __________ Email: ________________

Beneficiary: __________________ Ph: __________ Email: ________________

Trusts I've Set Up for Others

Name of Trust: ________________ Trust Bank: ________________________

Date of Trust: ________________ Location of Document: ________________

Trust Manager: ________________ Ph: __________ Email: ________________

Beneficiary: __________________ Ph: __________ Email: ________________

Beneficiary: __________________ Ph: __________ Email: ________________

Beneficiary: __________________ Ph: __________ Email: ________________

Beneficiary: __________________ Ph: __________ Email: ________________

Beneficiary: __________________ Ph: __________ Email: ________________

NOTES ____

Other Income

Source: ____________________ Monthly Income: ____________
Contact: ____________________ Ph: ____________________

Source: ____________________ Monthly Income: ____________
Contact: ____________________ Ph: ____________________

Source: ____________________ Monthly Income: ____________
Contact: ____________________ Ph: ____________________

Source: ____________________ Monthly Income: ____________
Contact: ____________________ Ph: ____________________

Source: ____________________ Monthly Income: ____________
Contact: ____________________ Ph: ____________________

Source: ____________________ Monthly Income: ____________
Contact: ____________________ Ph: ____________________

Source: ____________________ Monthly Income: ____________
Contact: ____________________ Ph: ____________________

Source: ____________________ Monthly Income: ____________
Contact: ____________________ Ph: ____________________

Source: ____________________ Monthly Income: ____________
Contact: ____________________ Ph: ____________________

NOTES ____

Business Partnerships and Corporations

Sole Proprietorship

Registered Owner: ______________ Ph: ____________ Email: ____________________

Business Name: ____________________________ DBA: ____________________

Industry: _________________ Date Formed: _____________ State Formed: ________

Business Address: __________________________ EIN: _____________________

Location of Business Documents: ____

Beneficiary: _______________ Ph: ____________ Email: ____________________

NOTES ____

____

____

____

____

____

Partnership

Legal Name of Company: _________________________

Owner: _________________________ Ph: ____________ Email: ___________________

Owner: _________________________ Ph: ____________ Email: ___________________

Industry: _________________ Date Formed: ______________ State Formed: ________

Business Address: __________________________ EIN: _____________________

Percentage of Business: ______ Location of Operating Agreement: ________________

Beneficiary: _______________ Ph: _______________ Email: ____________________

NOTES ____

____

____

____

____

____

Business Partnerships and Corporations

Limited Liability Corporation (LLC)

Legal Name of Company: ____________________

Industry: ______________ Date Formed: ________ State Formed: ________

Business Address: ______________________ EIN: ______________

Contact Person: ______________ Ph: __________ Email: ______________

Articles of Organization Location: ______________ Percentage of Business: _____

Is Ownership Transferable to Beneficiary after Death: Yes: _____ No: _____

Beneficiary: ________________ Ph: __________ Email: ______________

NOTES ____

____

____

____

____

Corporation

Legal Name of Company: ________________ Number of Shares: __________

Date Formed: ____________ State Formed: ____________

Business Address: ____________________ EIN: ________________

Contact Person: ______________ Ph: __________ Email: ______________

Location of Articles of Organization: __________________

Is Ownership Transferable to Beneficiary after Death: Yes: _____ No: _____

Beneficiary: ________________ Ph: __________ Email: ______________

NOTES ____

____

____

____

NOTES

Insurance

Primary Home Insurance

Company: ______________________ Policy Number: ___________________________

Agent: _________________________ Ph: ___________ Email: ___________________

Name Insured: __________________________________ Insured Amount: ___________

Location of Policy: _______________________________

Secondary Home Insurance

Company: ______________________ Policy Number: ___________________________

Agent: _________________________ Ph: ___________ Email: ___________________

Name Insured: __________________________________ Insured Amount: ___________

Location of Policy: _______________________________

Condo Insurance

Company: ______________________ Policy Number: ___________________________

Agent: _________________________ Ph: ___________ Email: ___________________

Name Insured: __________________________________ Insured Amount: ___________

Location of Policy: _______________________________

Vacation Home Insurance

Company: ______________________ Policy Number: ___________________________

Agent: _________________________ Ph: ___________ Email: ___________________

Name Insured: __________________________________ Insured Amount: ___________

Location of Policy: _______________________________

Time Share Insurance

Company: ______________________ Policy Number: ___________________________

Agent: _________________________ Ph: ___________ Email: ___________________

Name Insured: __________________________________ Insured Amount: ___________

Location of Policy: _______________________________

OTHER ____

____

____

____

____

Insurance

Umbrella Insurance

Company: ______________________ Policy Number: ____________________________

Agent: _________________________ Ph: ___________ Email: ____________________

Name Insured: __________________________________ Insured Amount: ___________

Location of Policy: _______________________________

Flood Insurance

Company: ______________________ Policy Number: ____________________________

Agent: _________________________ Ph: ___________ Email: ____________________

Name Insured: __________________________________ Insured Amount: ___________

Location of Policy: _______________________________

Renter's Insurance

Company: ______________________ Policy Number: ____________________________

Agent: _________________________ Ph: ___________ Email: ____________________

Name Insured: __________________________________ Insured Amount: ___________

Location of Policy: _______________________________

Additional Insurance

Company: ______________________ Policy Number: ____________________________

Agent: _________________________ Ph: ___________ Email: ____________________

Name Insured: __________________________________ Insured Amount: ___________

Location of Policy: _______________________________

Additional Insurance

Company: ______________________ Policy Number: ____________________________

Agent: _________________________ Ph: ___________ Email: ____________________

Name Insured: __________________________________ Insured Amount: ___________

Location of Policy: _______________________________

NOTES ____

Vehicle Insurance

Vehicle #1

Vehicle Make: ________________ Model: ________________ Year: _________

Company: ________________________ Policy Number: ___________________

Agent: ______________________ Ph: __________ Email: ________________

Name Insured: ______________________________ Insured Amount: _________

Location of Policy: ___________________________

Vehicle #2

Vehicle Make: ________________ Model: ________________ Year: _________

Company: ________________________ Policy Number: ___________________

Agent: ______________________ Ph: __________ Email: ________________

Name Insured: ______________________________ Insured Amount: _________

Location of Policy: ___________________________

Vehicle #3

Vehicle Make: ________________ Model: ________________ Year: _________

Company: ________________________ Policy Number: ___________________

Agent: ______________________ Ph: __________ Email: ________________

Name Insured: ______________________________ Insured Amount: _________

Location of Policy: ___________________________

Recreational Vehicle (RV)

Vehicle Make: ________________ Model: ________________ Year: _________

Company: ________________________ Policy Number: ___________________

Agent: ______________________ Ph: __________ Email: ________________

Name Insured: ______________________________ Insured Amount: _________

Location of Policy: ___________________________

OTHER ____

Medical Insurance

Major Medical Insurance

Company: ______________________ Ph: ____________ Website: __________________

Name Insured: __________________ Plan Name: ____________________________

Policy Number: _________________ Group: __________ HMO: ____ PPO: ____

Location of Policy: ______________

Supplemental Insurance

Company: ______________________ Ph: ____________ Website: __________________

Name Insured: __________________ Plan Name: ____________________________

Policy Number: _________________ Group: __________ HMO: ____ PPO: ____

Location of Policy: ______________

Disability Insurance

Agency: _______________________ Ph: ____________ Website: ________________

Name Insured: __________________ Policy Number: ________________________

Employment Insurance

Employer: ___________________________ Website: _________________________

Insurance Company: ___________________ Ph: ______________________________

Policy Number: _______________________ Location of Policy: ________________

Long-Term Health Care Insurance

Company: ___________________________ Policy Number: ____________________

Ph: ________________________________ Website: _________________________

Location of Policy: ___________________

Medicare

Medicare Number: _____________________ Ph: ______________________________

Social Security Number:________________ Location of Policy: ________________

Hospital: Part: A: ______ B: ______ Medical: Part: A: ______ B: _______

Basic Accounts to Cancel

Electric Company: ______________ Account Number: _________________
Username: ______________________ Password: _______________________
Website: ________________________ Ph: ____________________________
Auto Pay: Yes: _____ No: _____ Bank Account/Card: _______________

Gas Company: _________________ Account Number: _________________
Username: ______________________ Password: _______________________
Website: ________________________ Ph: ____________________________
Auto Pay: Yes: _____ No: _____ Bank Account/Card: _______________

Water Company: _______________ Account Number: _________________
Username: ______________________ Password: _______________________
Website: ________________________ Ph: ____________________________
Auto Pay: Yes: _____ No: _____ Bank Account/Card: _______________

Curbside Collection: ____________ Account Number: _________________
Username: ______________________ Password: _______________________
Website: ________________________ Ph: ____________________________
Auto Pay: Yes: _____ No: _____ Bank Account/Card: _______________

Cable Company: _______________ Account Number: _________________
Username: ______________________ Password: _______________________
Website: ________________________ Ph: ____________________________
Auto Pay: Yes: _____ No: _____ Bank Account/Card: _______________

Internet Provider: _____________ Account Number: _________________
Username: ______________________ Password: _______________________
Website: ________________________ Ph: ____________________________
Auto Pay: Yes: _____ No: _____ Bank Account/Card: _______________

Home Phone: __________________ Account Number: _________________
Username: ______________________ Password: _______________________
Website: ________________________ Ph: ____________________________
Auto Pay: Yes: _____ No: _____ Bank Account/Card: _______________

Basic Accounts to Cancel

Cell Phone: ____________________
Username: ____________________
Website: ____________________
Auto Pay: Yes: _____ No: _____

Account Number: ____________________
Password: ____________________
Ph: ____________________
Bank Account/Card: ____________________

Home Security: ____________________
Username: ____________________
Website: ____________________
Auto Pay: Yes: _____ No: _____

Account Number: ____________________
Password: ____________________
Ph: ____________________
Bank Account/Card: ____________________

Lawn Service: ____________________
Username: ____________________
Website: ____________________
Auto Pay: Yes: _____ No: _____

Account Number: ____________________
Password: ____________________
Ph: ____________________
Bank Account/Card: ____________________

Pool Service: ____________________
Username: ____________________
Website: ____________________
Auto Pay: Yes: _____ No: _____

Account Number: ____________________
Password: ____________________
Ph: ____________________
Bank Account/Card: ____________________

Pest Control: ____________________
Username: ____________________
Website: ____________________
Auto Pay: Yes: _____ No: _____

Account Number: ____________________
Password: ____________________
Ph: ____________________
Bank Account/Card: ____________________

Newspaper: ____________________
Username: ____________________
Website: ____________________
Auto Pay: Yes: _____ No: _____

Account Number: ____________________
Password: ____________________
Ph: ____________________
Bank Account/Card: ____________________

Magazines/Book Club: __________
Username: ____________________
Website: ____________________
Auto Pay: Yes: _____ No: _____

Account Number: ____________________
Password: ____________________
Ph: ____________________
Bank Account/Card: ____________________

Basic Accounts to Cancel

Gym: ________________________
Username: ______________________
Website: _______________________
Auto Pay: Yes: _____ No: _____

Account Number: ______________
Password: _____________________
Ph: __________________________
Bank Account/Card: ____________

HOA: ________________________
Username: ______________________
Website: _______________________
Auto Pay: Yes: _____ No: _____

Account Number: ______________
Password: _____________________
Ph: __________________________
Bank Account/Card: ____________

Country Club: ________________
Username: ______________________
Website: _______________________
Auto Pay: Yes: _____ No: _____

Account Number: ______________
Password: _____________________
Ph: __________________________
Bank Account/Card: ____________

Triple A: ______________
Username: ______________________
Website: _______________________
Auto Pay: Yes: _____ No: _____

Account Number: ______________
Password: _____________________
Ph: __________________________
Bank Account/Card: ____________

TV Streaming Service: _________
Username: ______________________
Website: _______________________
Auto Pay: Yes: _____ No: _____

Account Number: ______________
Password: _____________________
Ph: __________________________
Bank Account/Card: ____________

TV Streaming Service: _________
Username: ______________________
Website: _______________________
Auto Pay: Yes: _____ No: _____

Account Number: ______________
Password: _____________________
Ph: __________________________
Bank Account/Card: ____________

Storage Unit:________________
Username: ______________________
Website: _______________________
Auto Pay: Yes: _____ No: _____

Account Number
Password: _____________________
Ph: __________________________
Bank Account/Card: ____________

Basic Accounts to Cancel

Other Insurance: ______________
Username: ____________________
Auto Pay: Yes: _____ No: _____
Website: ______________________

Account Number: ________________
Password: _____________________
Bank Account/Card: _____________
Ph: ___________________________

Medicare Payments: ___________
Username: ____________________
Auto Pay: Yes: _____ No: _____
Website: ______________________

Account Number: ________________
Password: _____________________
Bank Account/Card: _____________
Ph: ___________________________

Social Security Payments: _______
Username: ____________________
Auto Pay: Yes: _____ No: _____
Website: ______________________

Account Number: ________________
Password: _____________________
Bank Account/Card: _____________
Ph: ___________________________

Disability Payments: ___________
Username: ____________________
Auto Pay: Yes: _____ No: _____
Website: ______________________

Account Number: ________________
Password: _____________________
Bank Account/Card: _____________
Ph: ___________________________

Veteran's Benefits: ____________
Username: ____________________
Auto Pay: Yes: _____ No: _____
Website: ______________________

Account Number: ________________
Password: _____________________
Bank Account/Card: _____________
Ph: ______________________

Other Service: _______________
Username: ____________________
Auto Pay: Yes: _____ No: _____
Website: ______________________

Account Number: ________________
Password: _____________________
Bank Account/Card: _____________
Ph: ___________________________

Other Service: _______________
Username: ____________________
Auto Pay: Yes: _____ No: _____
Website: ______________________

Account Number: ________________
Password: _____________________
Bank Account/Card: _____________
Ph: ___________________________

Other Automatic *Annual* Renewal Accounts to Cancel

LifeLock
Auto Insurance
Health Insurance
Home Insurance
Credit Cards
Safe Deposit Box

Professional Fees
Legal/Professional Retainers
Genealogy Memberships
Other Paid Memberships
Storage Unit
Big Box Supermarkets (i.e. Costco)

OTHER

1. ____________________
2. ____________________
3. ____________________
4. ____________________
5. ____________________
6. ____________________
7. ____________________
8. ____________________
9. ____________________
10. ____________________

NOTES ____

***Without cancelling auto-pay arrangements, your estate will continue to be charged.**

Credit Card Bank/Airline Reward Programs

Credit Card/Banking Rewards

Bank: ____________________ Account Number: ____________________
Username: ____________________ Password: ____________________
Beneficiary: ____________________ Ph: ____________ Email: ____________

Bank: ____________________ Account Number: ____________________
Username: ____________________ Password: ____________________
Beneficiary: ____________________ Ph: ____________ Email: ____________

Bank: ____________________ Account Number: ____________________
Username: ____________________ Password: ____________________
Beneficiary: ____________________ Ph: ____________ Email: ____________

Bank: ____________________ Account Number: ____________________
Username: ____________________ Password: ____________________
Beneficiary: ____________________ Ph: ____________ Email: ____________

Airline Reward Programs

Airline: ____________________ Account Number: ____________________
Username: ____________________ Password: ____________________
Benefits: ____________________ Estimated Rewards/Points: ____________
Beneficiary: ____________________ Ph: ____________ Email: ____________

Airline: ____________________ Account Number: ____________________
Username: ____________________ Password: ____________________
Benefits: ____________________ Estimated Rewards/Points: ____________
Beneficiary: ____________________ Ph: ____________ Email: ____________

Airline: ____________________ Account Number: ____________________
Username: ____________________ Password: ____________________
Benefits: ____________________ Estimated Rewards/Points: ____________
Beneficiary: ____________________ Ph: ____________ Email: ____________

Passwords

URL:	User Name:	Password:
URL: ________________	User Name: ______________	Password: ___________
URL: ________________	User Name: ______________	Password: ___________
URL: ________________	User Name: ______________	Password: ___________
URL: ________________	User Name: ______________	Password: ___________
URL: ________________	User Name: ______________	Password: ___________
URL: ________________	User Name: ______________	Password: ___________
URL: ________________	User Name: ______________	Password: ___________
URL: ________________	User Name: ______________	Password: ___________
URL: ________________	User Name: ______________	Password: ___________
URL: ________________	User Name: ______________	Password: ___________
URL: ________________	User Name: ______________	Password: ___________
URL: ________________	User Name: ______________	Password: ___________
URL: ________________	User Name: ______________	Password: ___________
URL: ________________	User Name: ______________	Password: ___________
URL: ________________	User Name: ______________	Password: ___________
URL: ________________	User Name: ______________	Password: ___________
URL: ________________	User Name: ______________	Password: ___________
URL: ________________	User Name: ______________	Password: ___________
URL: ________________	User Name: ______________	Password: ___________
URL: ________________	User Name: ______________	Password: ___________

Social Media Accounts and Passwords

Personal Email
Username: ____________________ Password: ____________________

Work Email
Username: ____________________ Password: ____________________

Facebook
Username: ____________________ Password: ____________________

Instagram
Username: ____________________ Password: ____________________

YouTube
Username: ____________________ Password: ____________________

WhatsApp
Username: ____________________ Password: ____________________

Twitter
Username: ____________________ Password: ____________________

Snap Chat
Username: ____________________ Password: ____________________

Linkedin
Username: ____________________ Password: ____________________

Telegram
Username: ____________________ Password: ____________________

Reddit
Username: ____________________ Password: ____________________

Other:____________________
Username: ____________________ Password: ____________________

Other:____________________
Username: ____________________ Password: ____________________

Other:____________________
Username: ____________________ Password: ____________________

Miscellaneous

Pet Care

Name of the Person to Care for My Pet(s): ______________________

Ph: __________ Cell: __________ Email: ______________

Special Care Instructions: ______________________

____

____

Veterinarian: ______________ Website: ______________

Ph: ______________ Address: ______________

Locations of Keys

House: ______________ Cars: ______________

Condo: ______________ Time Share: ______________

Vacation Home: ______________ Office: ______________

Boat: ______________ Motorcycle: ______________

Safe Deposit Box: ______________ Safe Key/Code: ______________

Other: ______________ Other: ______________

Storage Unit

Name: ______________ Address: ______________

Unit Number: ______________ Code: ______ Key Location: ______________

Marina

Name: ______________ Address: ______________

Slip Number: ______________ Code: ______ Key Location: ______________

OTHER

1. ______________________
2. ______________________
3. ______________________
4. ______________________
5. ______________________
6. ______________________

Miscellaneous

Safe Contents

1. ______________________ 6. ______________________
2. ______________________ 7. ______________________
3. ______________________ 8. ______________________
4. ______________________ 9. ______________________
5. ______________________ 10. ______________________

Safe Deposit Box Contents

1. ______________________ 6. ______________________
2. ______________________ 7. ______________________
3. ______________________ 8. ______________________
4. ______________________ 9. ______________________
5. ______________________ 10. ______________________

Fire Arms

Location: ______________________

1. ______________________ Serial Number: ______________________
2. ______________________ Serial Number: ______________________
3. ______________________ Serial Number: ______________________
4. ______________________ Serial Number: ______________________

Patents: ______________________ Location: ______________________

Copyrights: ______________________ Location: ______________________

Trademarks: ______________________ Location: ______________________

Titles and Deeds: ______________________ Location: ______________________

OTHER

1. ____
2. ____
3. ____
4. ____
5. ____

NOTES

NOTES

NOTES

Love Letter

To: ______________________________

To: ______________________________

Love Letter

To: ______________________________

To: ______________________________

My Greatest Achievements Were…

1. ______________________________

2. ______________________________

3. ______________________________

4. ______________________________

I Am Most Proud of...

1.

2.

3.

4.

I'm Glad That I...

1.

2.

3.

4.

I Wish I Had...

1.

2.

3.

4.

Regret... *Apologies...*

1.

2.

3.

4.

My Fondest Memories...

1.

2.

3.

4.

What I'm Most Thankful For...

1.

2.

3.

4.

When I'm Gone, I Hope That...

1.

2.

3.

4.

Additional Thoughts I Want to Share...

Final Notes